ke to see how far I can take it

Absinthe make your a whore

see the whites of my eyes
I'm a stuntman
see
the whites of my eyes

I see a lover flash me before on her knees

Get your boots in man
get your boots in girl

**K**

Empire [6]

Shoot The Runner [9]

Last Trip (In Flight) [14]

Me Plus One [20]

Sun Rise Light Flies [24]

Apnoea [29]

By My Side [32]

Stuntman [38]

Seek & Destroy [45]

British Legion [48]

The Doberman [53]

# EMPIRE

Words by Sergio Pizzorno
Music by Sergio Pizzorno and Christopher Karloff

© 2006 EMI Music Publishing Ltd, London WC2H 0QY

nights out on the cor - ner. }
see that I'm the one. }

Tell me that you've seen a ghost, I tell you one to fear the most.

STOP.

I said it's hap-pening a - gain.___

We're all wast - ing a-way.

We're all wast - ing A - WAY.___

Synth. Bass arr. Gtr. plays Fig. 2
Synth. Strings arr. Gtr. play Fig 3

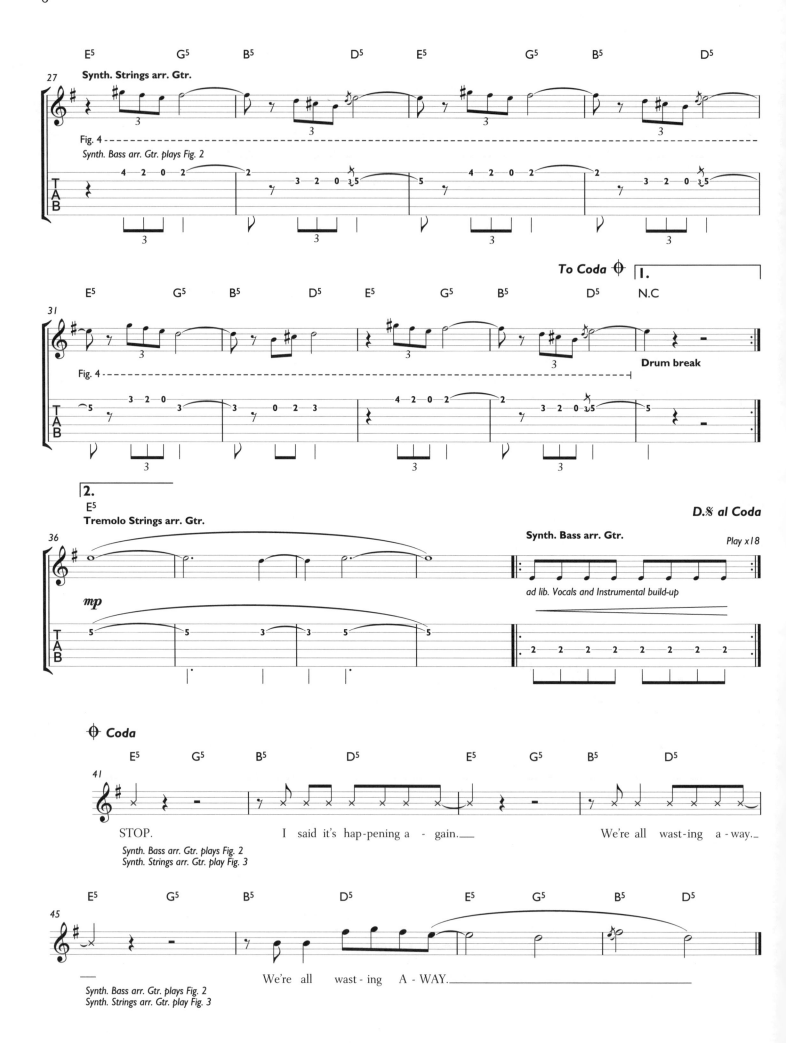

# SHOOT THE RUNNER

### Words and Music by Sergio Pizzorno

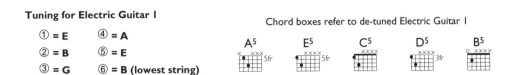

Shh.

Ah.

Fig. 1 - - - - - - - - - - - - - - - - - - - - - - - - - - - - - - - - - - - - - - - - - - - - -

Shoot the run-ner,— shoot, shoot the run-ner.— I'm a king— and she's my queen.

*Elec. Gtr. 1 plays Fig. 1*

© 2006 EMI Music Publishing Ltd, London WC2H 0QY

Shoot the run-ner,_ shoot, shoot the run-ner. I'm a king_ and she's my queen. She's my queen,_ BITCH.
whore.

*Elec. Gtr. 1 plays Fig. 1*
*Backing Vox. sing Fig. 1*

12

Kings,___ Kings may come___ and then go, by this sword_ you must know___ that all things come_ and then_

*Elec. Gtr. 1 plays Fig. 1*
*Elec. Gtr. 2 ad-lib. sim.*
*Backing Vox. sings Figs. 1+2*

*Elec. Gtr. 1 plays Fig. 1*
*Backing Vox. sings Fig. 2*

pass, live your days_ like_ the last.___ La la la la la___ la.___

*Elec. Gtr. 1 plays Fig. 1*
*Backing Vox. sing Figs. 1+2*

You're my_ queen. I say now, shoot, shoot the run-ner.___ 'Cos I'm a king and you're my queen, BITCH.

*Elec. Gtr. 1 plays Fig. 1*
*Backing Vox. sings Fig. 2*

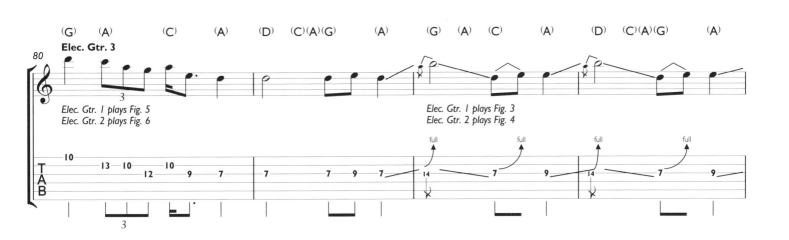

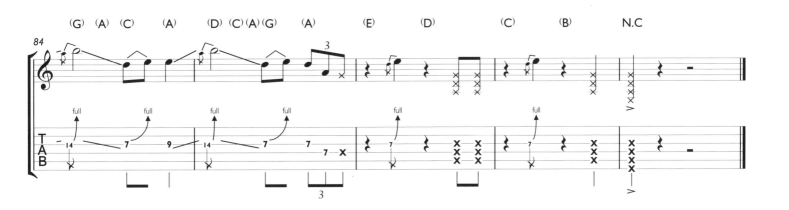

# LAST TRIP (IN FLIGHT)

Words and Music by Sergio Pizzorno

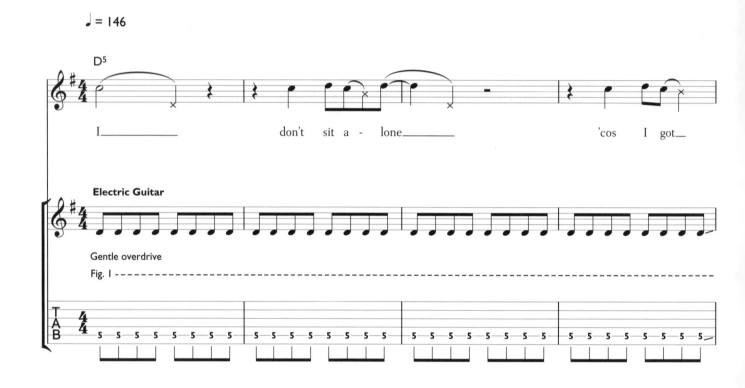

© 2006 EMI Music Publishing Ltd, London WC2H 0QY

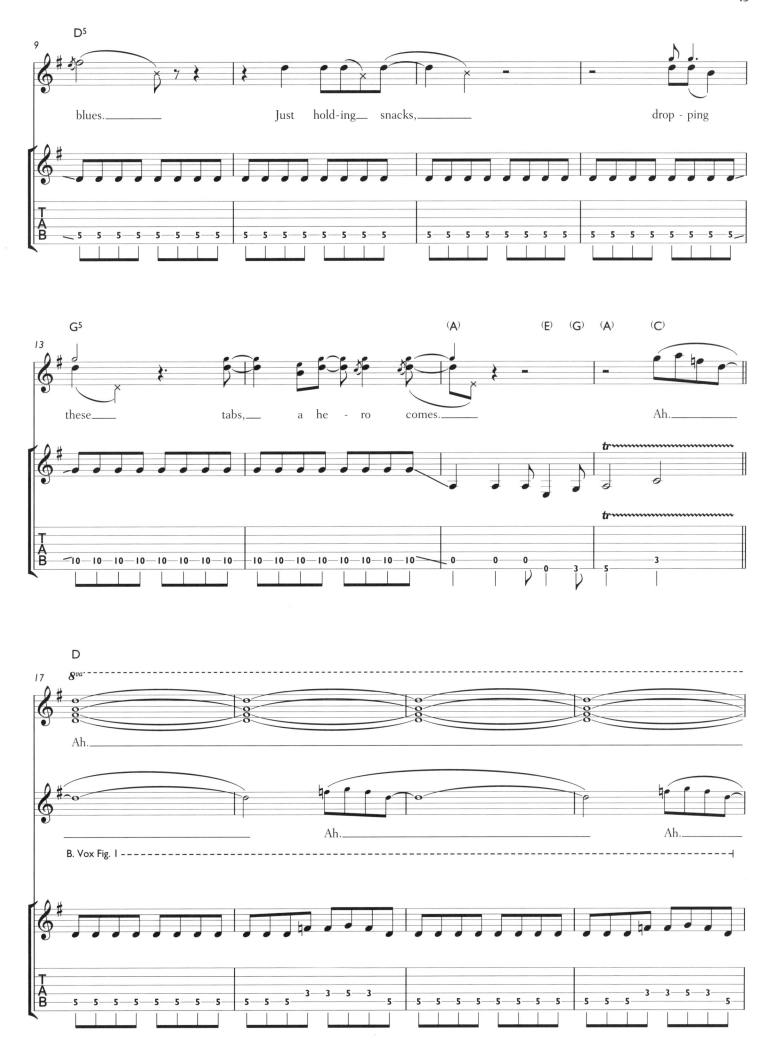

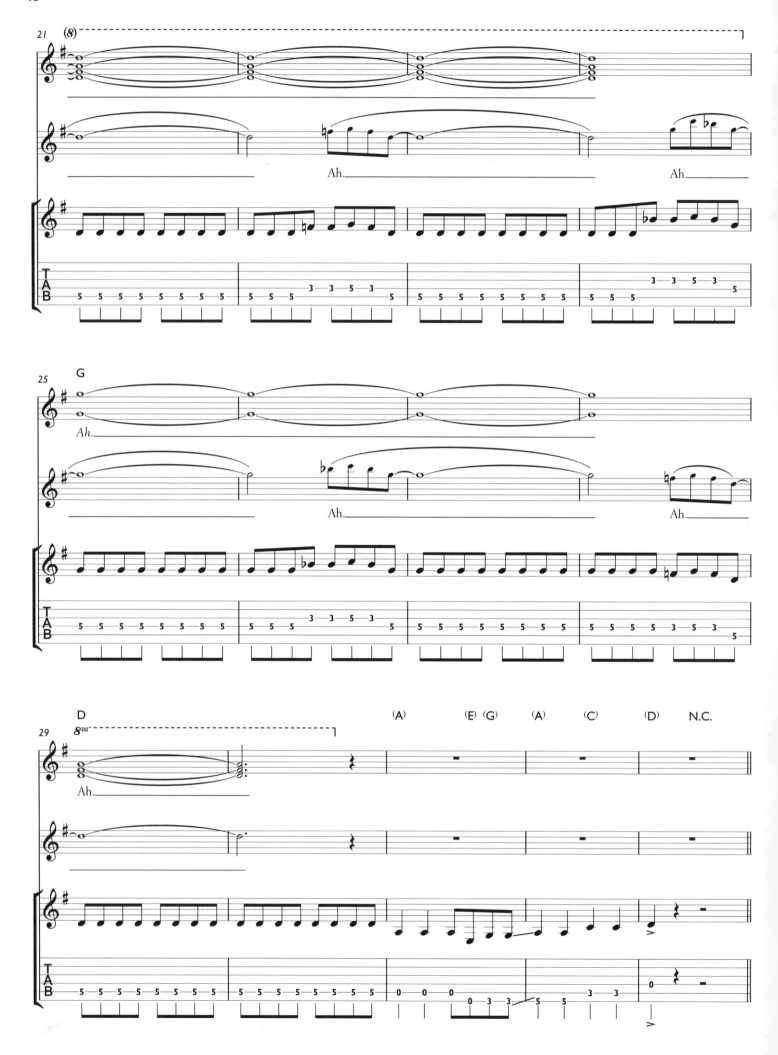

# ME PLUS ONE

Words and Music by Sergio Pizzorno

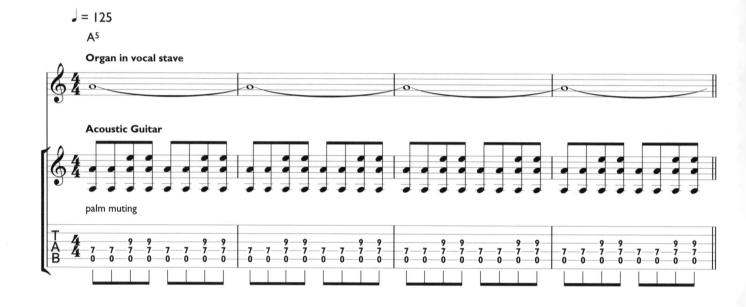

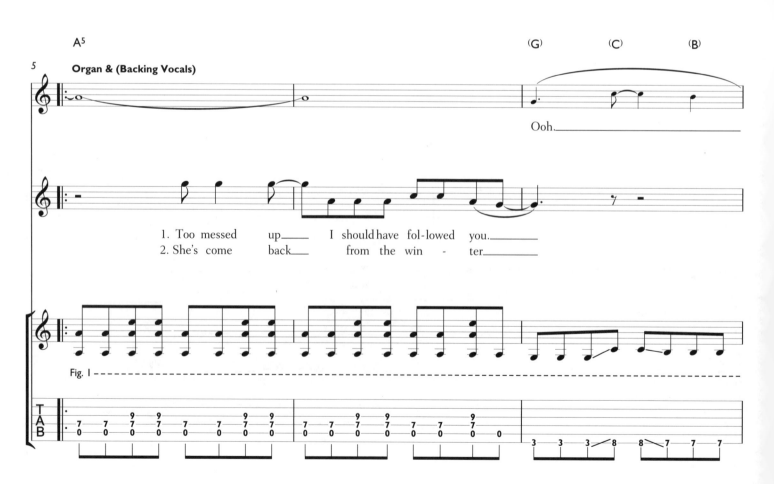

1. Too messed up___ I should have fol-lowed you.___
2. She's come back___ from the win - ter___

Ooh.___

© 2006 EMI Music Publishing Ltd, London WC2H 0QY

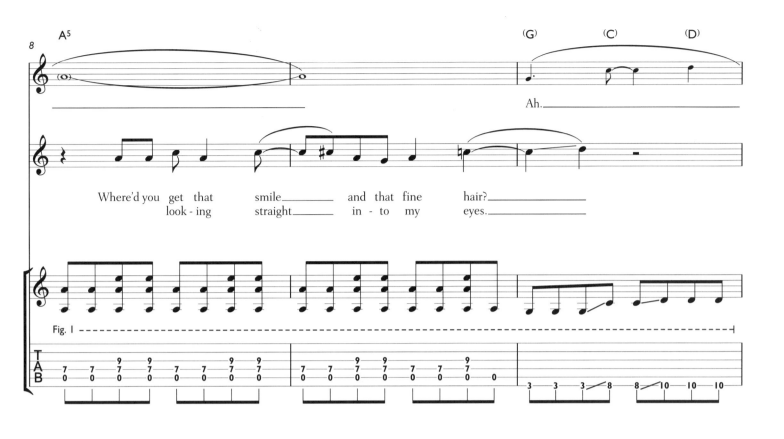

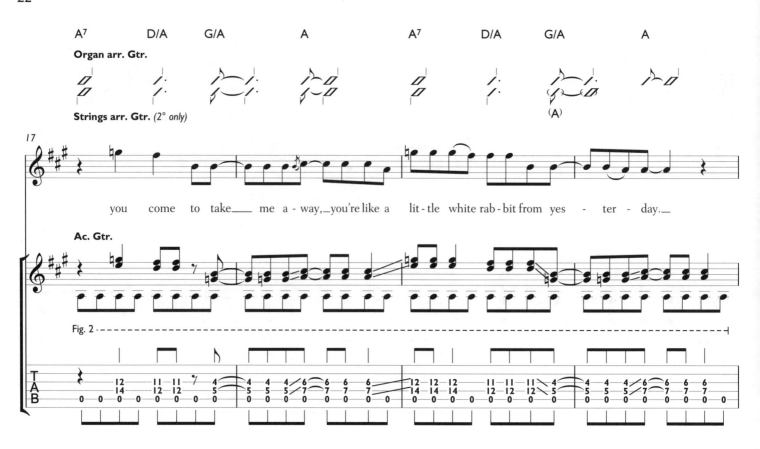

you come to take___ me a-way,___ you're like a lit-tle white rab-bit from yes - ter - day.___

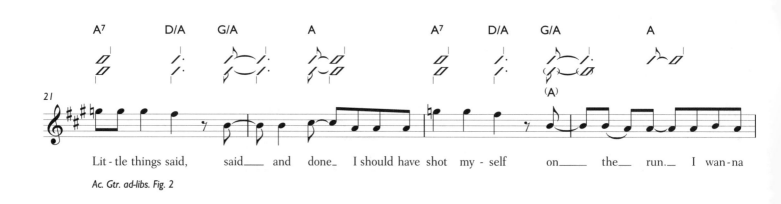

Lit - tle things said, said___ and done___ I should have shot my-self on___ the___ run.___ I wan-na

love, love,___ love.___ I wan-na love, love,___ love___ right now.___ I wan-na

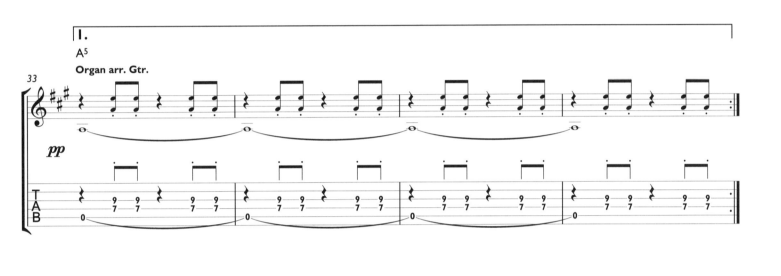

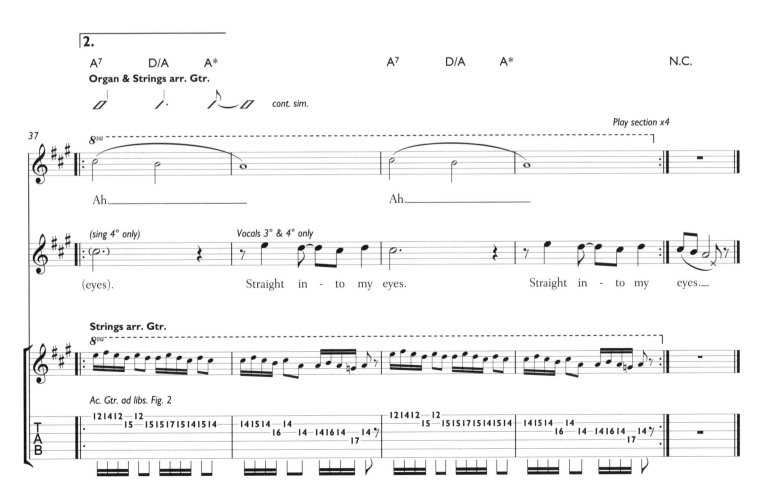

# SUN/RISE/LIGHT/FLIES

*Words and Music by Sergio Pizzorno*

© 2006 EMI Music Publishing Ltd, London WC2H 0QY

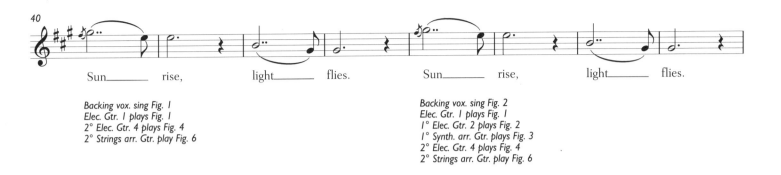

**40**

Sun_____ rise, light_____ flies. Sun_____ rise, light_____ flies.

*Backing vox. sing Fig. 1*
*Elec. Gtr. 1 plays Fig. 1*
*2° Elec. Gtr. 4 plays Fig. 4*
*2° Strings arr. Gtr. play Fig. 6*

*Backing vox. sing Fig. 2*
*Elec. Gtr. 1 plays Fig. 1*
*1° Elec. Gtr. 2 plays Fig. 2*
*1° Synth. arr. Gtr. plays Fig. 3*
*2° Elec. Gtr. 4 plays Fig. 4*
*2° Strings arr. Gtr. play Fig. 6*

**To Coda** ⊕

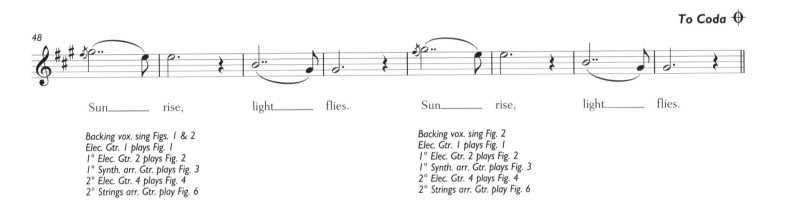

**48**

Sun_____ rise, light_____ flies. Sun_____ rise, light_____ flies.

*Backing vox. sing Figs. 1 & 2*
*Elec. Gtr. 1 plays Fig. 1*
*1° Elec. Gtr. 2 plays Fig. 2*
*1° Synth. arr. Gtr. plays Fig. 3*
*2° Elec. Gtr. 4 plays Fig. 4*
*2° Strings arr. Gtr. play Fig. 6*

*Backing vox. sing Fig. 2*
*Elec. Gtr. 1 plays Fig. 1*
*1° Elec. Gtr. 2 plays Fig. 2*
*1° Synth. arr. Gtr. plays Fig. 3*
*2° Elec. Gtr. 4 plays Fig. 4*
*2° Strings arr. Gtr. play Fig. 6*

**1.2.3.**     **4.**    ***D.%% al Coda***

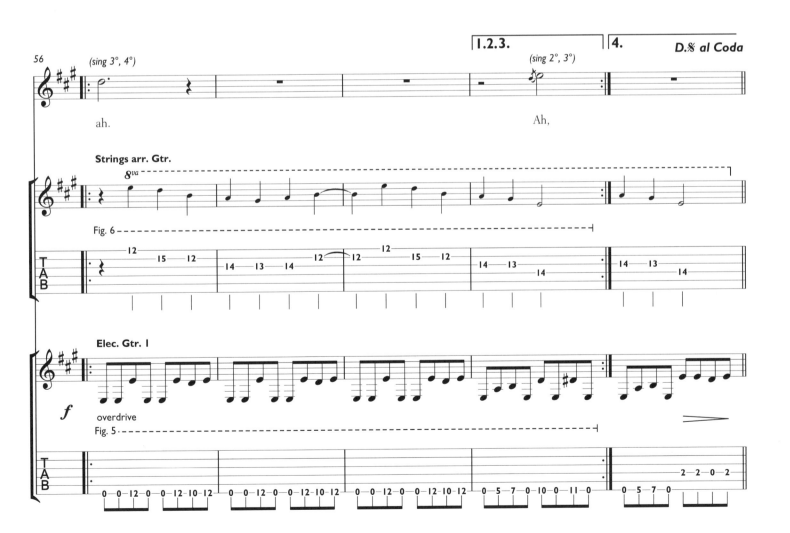

**56** *(sing 3°, 4°)*        *(sing 2°, 3°)*

ah.       Ah,

**Strings arr. Gtr.**

**Elec. Gtr. 1**

*f* overdrive
Fig. 5

⊕ *Coda*

**Elec. Gtr. 3**

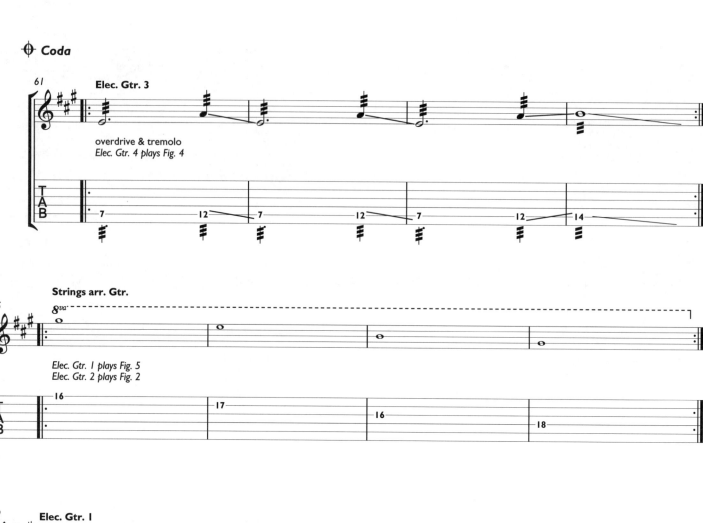

overdrive & tremolo
*Elec. Gtr. 4 plays Fig. 4*

**Strings arr. Gtr.**

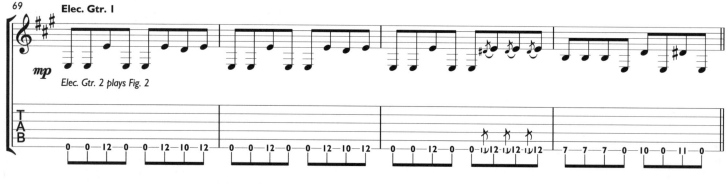

*Elec. Gtr. 1 plays Fig. 5*
*Elec. Gtr. 2 plays Fig. 2*

**Elec. Gtr. 1**

*Elec. Gtr. 2 plays Fig. 2*

**Elec. Gtr. 1** (*1° only*)

*Play section x3 to finish*

**Elec. Gtr. 3**

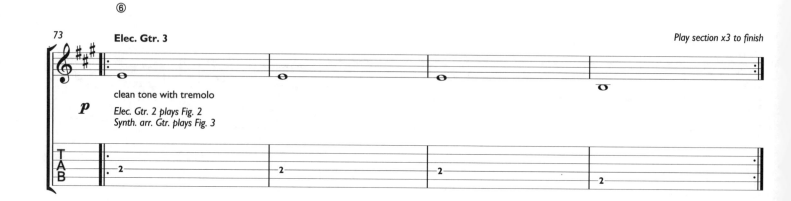

clean tone with tremolo
*Elec. Gtr. 2 plays Fig. 2*
*Synth. arr. Gtr. plays Fig. 3*

# APNOEA

*Words and Music by Sergio Pizzorno*

© 2006 EMI Music Publishing Ltd, London WC2H 0QY

# BY MY SIDE

Music & Words by Sergio Pizzorno
String arrangement by Christopher Karloff

© 2006 EMI Music Publishing Ltd, London WC2H 0QY

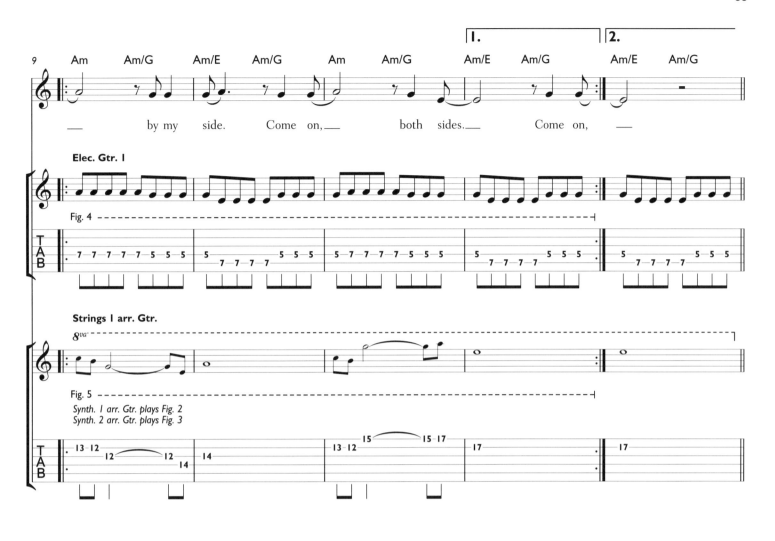

by my side. Come on,___ both sides.___ Come on, ___

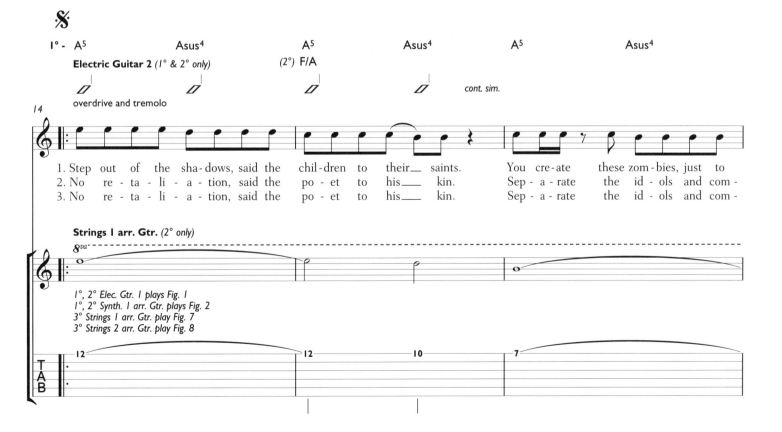

1. Step out of the sha-dows, said the chil-dren to their___ saints. You cre-ate these zom-bies, just to
2. No re-ta-li-a-tion, said the po-et to his___ kin. Sep-a-rate the id-ols and com-
3. No re-ta-li-a-tion, said the po-et to his___ kin. Sep-a-rate the id-ols and com-

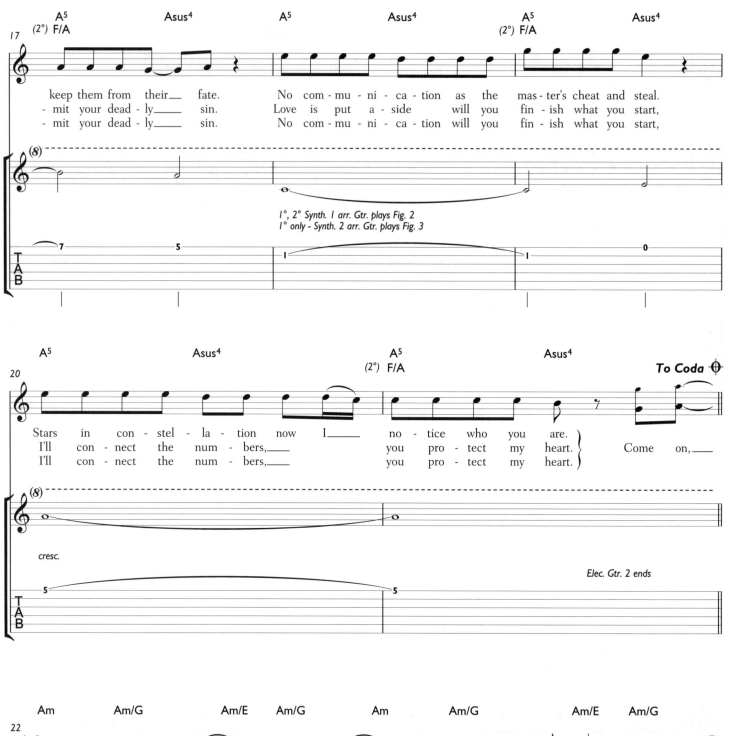

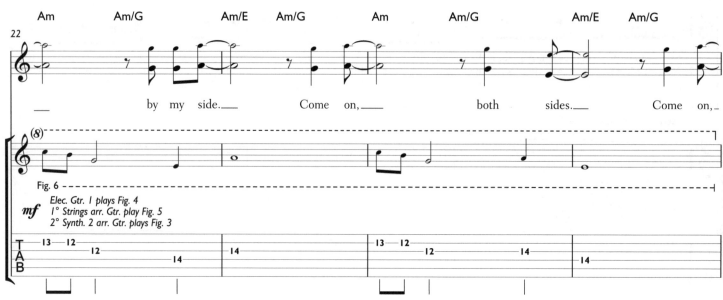

by my side.___ Come on,___ both sides.___ (1°) Come on.___

*Elec. Gtr. 1 plays Fig. 4*
*1° Strings 1 arr. Gtr. play Fig. 5*
*2° Strings 1 arr. Gtr. play Fig. 6*
*2° Synth. 2 arr. Gtr. plays Fig. 3*

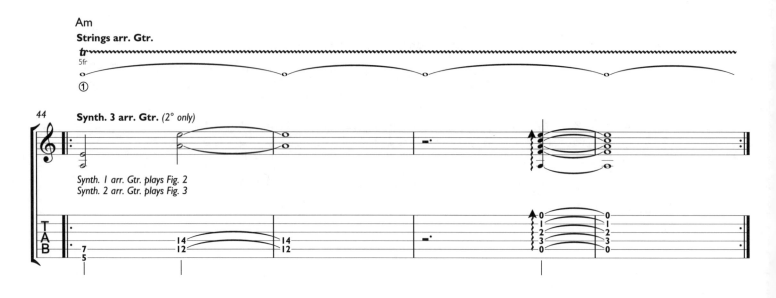

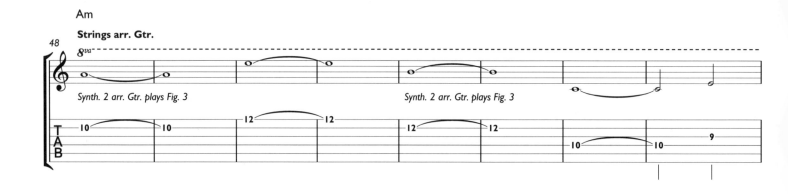

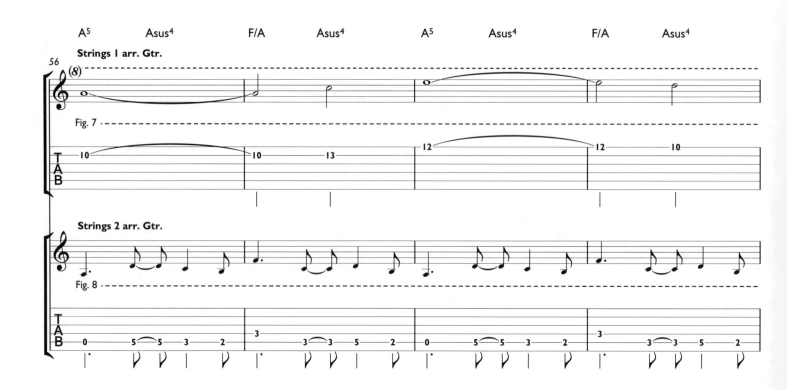

D.%. al Coda

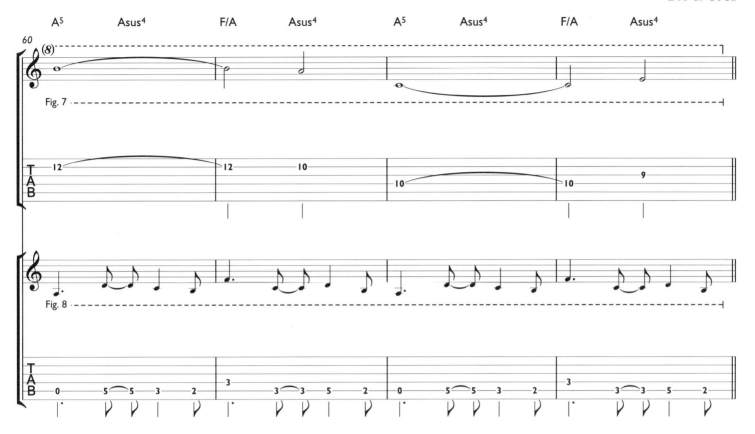

**Coda**

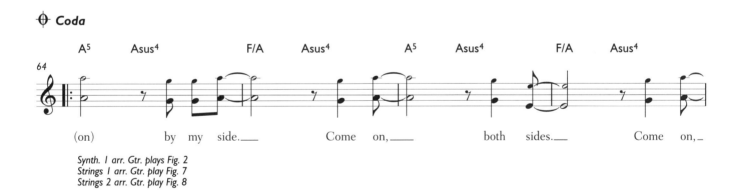

(on)      by   my   side.___     Come   on,___      both   sides.___      Come   on,__

*Synth. 1 arr. Gtr. plays Fig. 2*
*Strings 1 arr. Gtr. play Fig. 7*
*Strings 2 arr. Gtr. play Fig. 8*

___      by   my   side.___     Come   on,___      both   sides.___

*Synth. 1 arr. Gtr. plays Fig. 2*
*Strings 1 arr. Gtr. play Fig. 7*
*Strings 2 arr. Gtr. play Fig. 8*

# STUNTMAN

Words by Sergio Pizzorno
Music by Sergio Pizzorno and Christopher Karloff

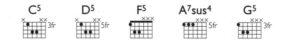

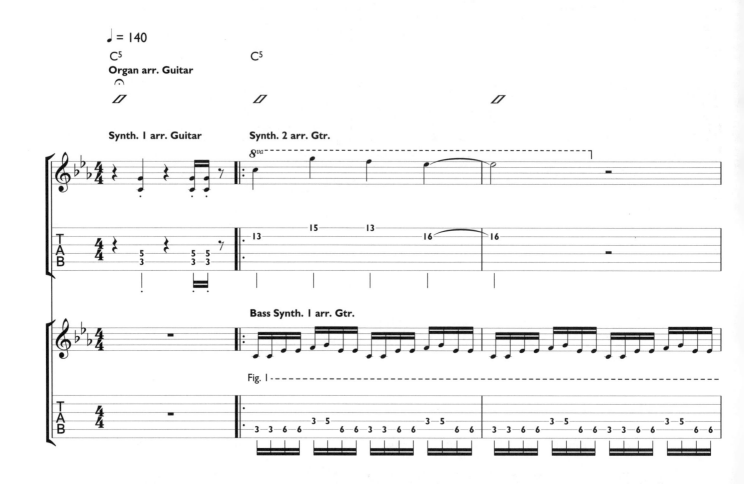

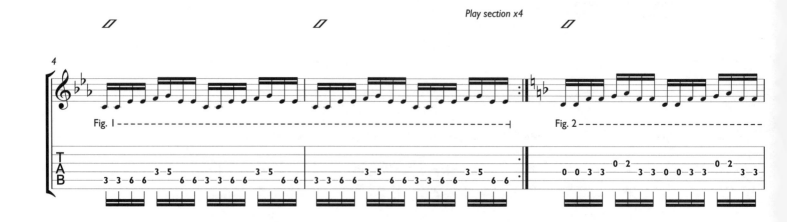

© 2006 EMI Music Publishing Ltd, London WC2H 0QY

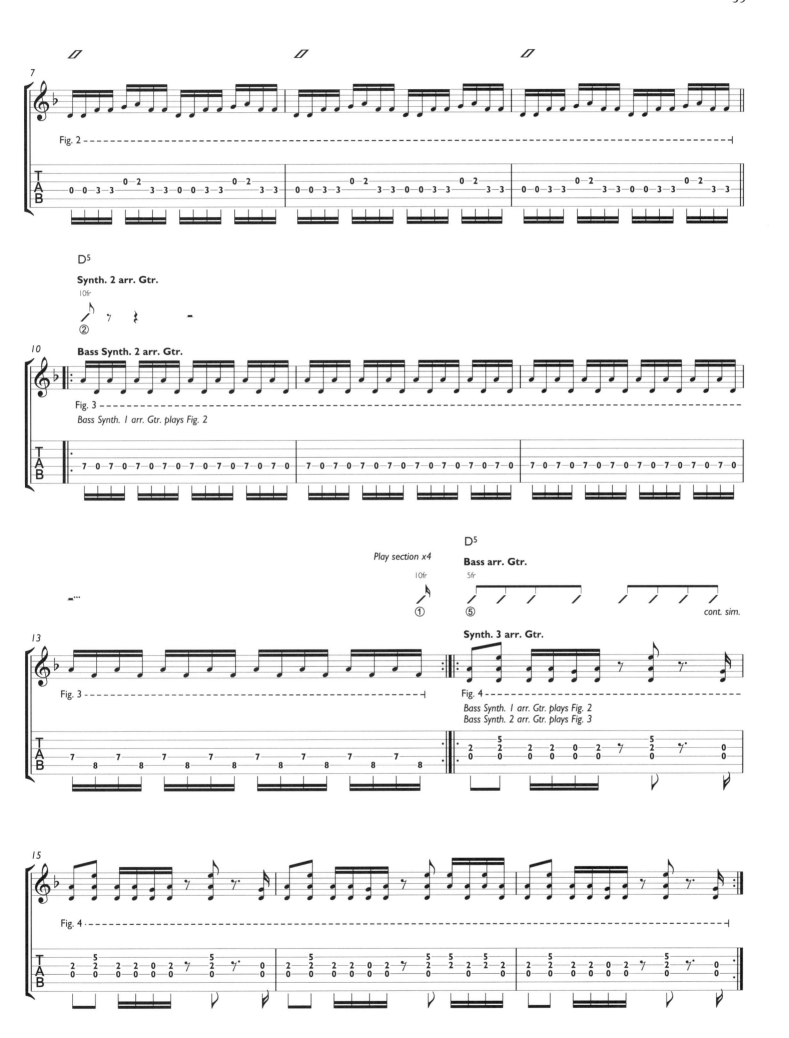

D⁵

**Bass arr. Gtr.**

cont. sim.

**18**

1. No_ map_ look-ing for the one I____ love,_ 'cause the one I____ love_ is here._  And
2. More_ cuts_ ta - ken for the one in____ si - lence now he sits_ be - tween my ears._  His

*Bass Synth. 2 arr. Gtr. plays Fig. 3*
*2° Synth. 3 arr. Gtr. ad-lib. Fig. 4*

**22**

no____ map_ look-ing for the one who_ stands, 'cause he's arm-ing me_from fear.
moves_ in_ mad - ness how I love the_ rush, and could you wipe a - way these tears?

*Bass Synth. 2 arr. Gtr. plays Fig. 3*
*2° Synth. 3 arr. Gtr. ad-lib Fig. 4*

**26**

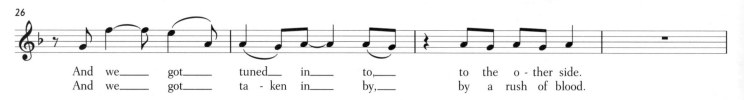

And we____ got____ tuned_ in_ to,_  to the o - ther side.
And we____ got____ ta - ken in_ by,_  by a rush of blood.

*Bass Synth. 1 arr. Gtr. plays Fig. 2*
*Bass Synth. 2 arr. Gtr. plays Fig. 3*
*Synth. 3 arr. Gtr. plays Fig. 4*

**30**

N.C.

Lives_ spent_ dig - ging_ holes_ to the,_  to the ones you hide._ ⎫
My_ train's_ leav - ing_ now_ how I,_  how I wish I could._ ⎭

*Bass Synth 1 arr. Gtr. plays Fig. 2*
*Bass Synth 2 arr. Gtr. plays Fig. 3*
*Synth. 3 arr. Gtr. plays Fig. 4*

*End all instrumental Figs.*
*2° End Bass arr. Gtr.*

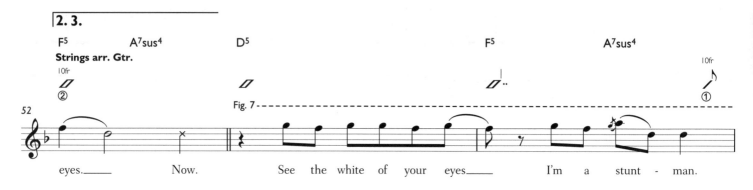

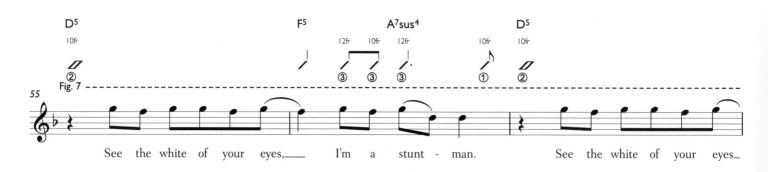

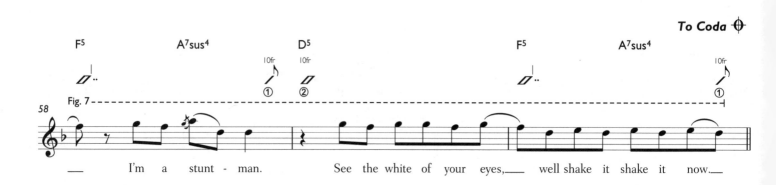

⊕ **Coda**

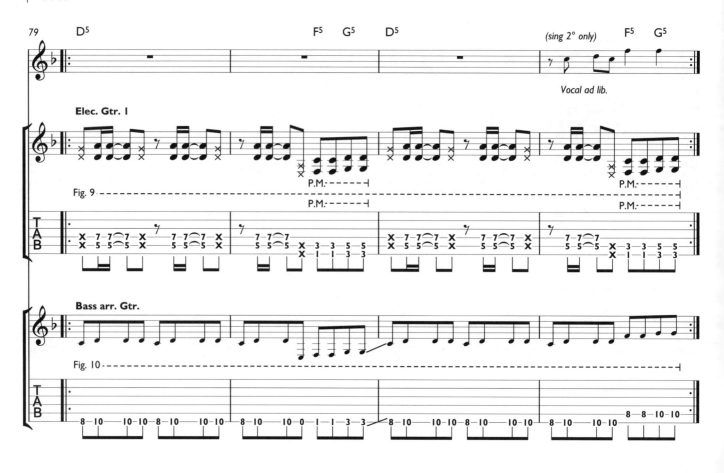

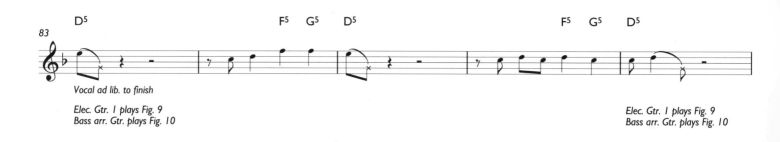

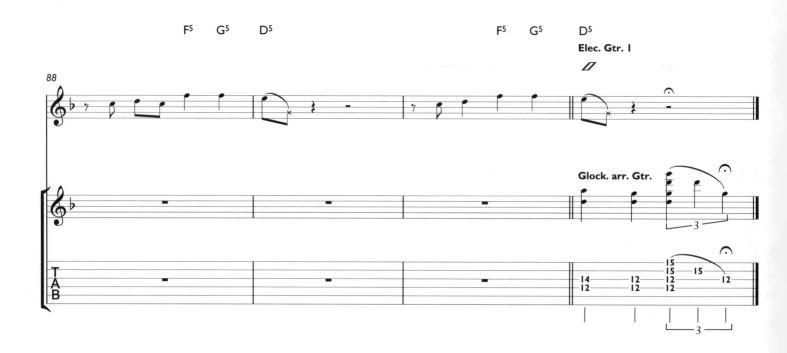

# SEEK & DESTROY

Words and Music by Sergio Pizzorno

© 2006 EMI Music Publishing Ltd, London WC2H 0QY

46

# BRITISH LEGION

### Words and Music by Sergio Pizzorno

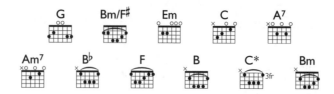

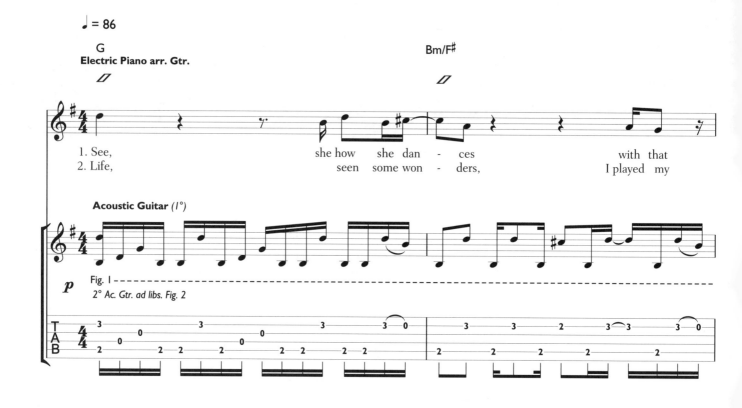

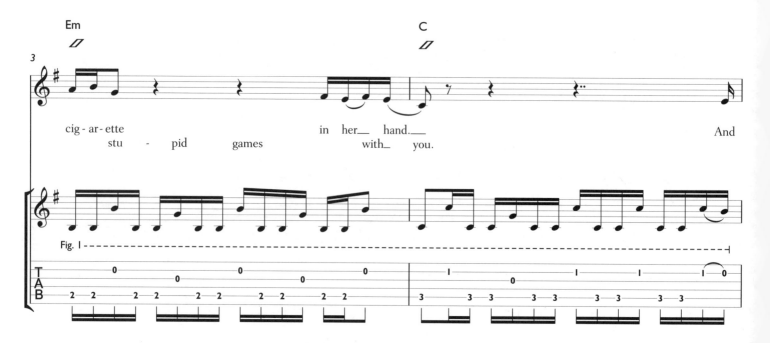

© 2006 EMI Music Publishing Ltd, London WC2H 0QY

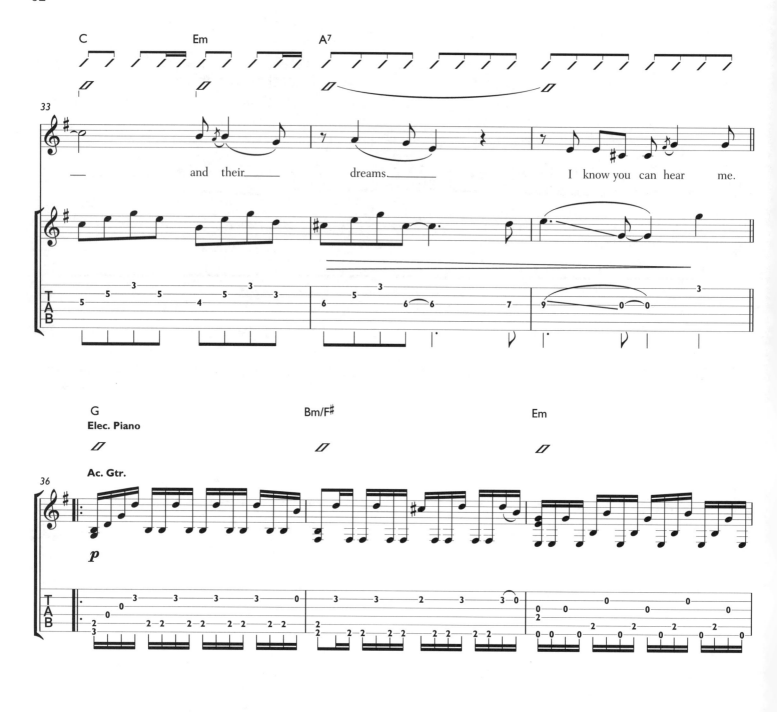

and their_____ dreams_____ I know you can hear me.

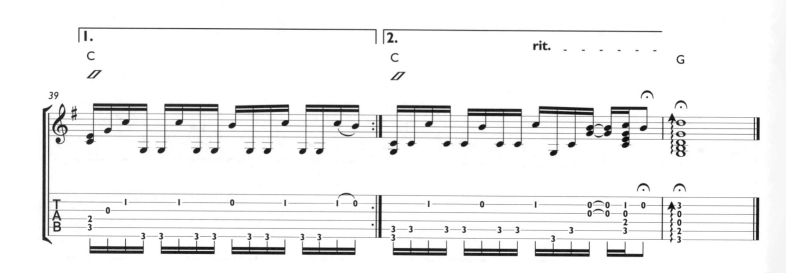

# THE DOBERMAN

### Words and Music by Sergio Pizzorno

© 2006 EMI Music Publishing Ltd, London WC2H 0QY

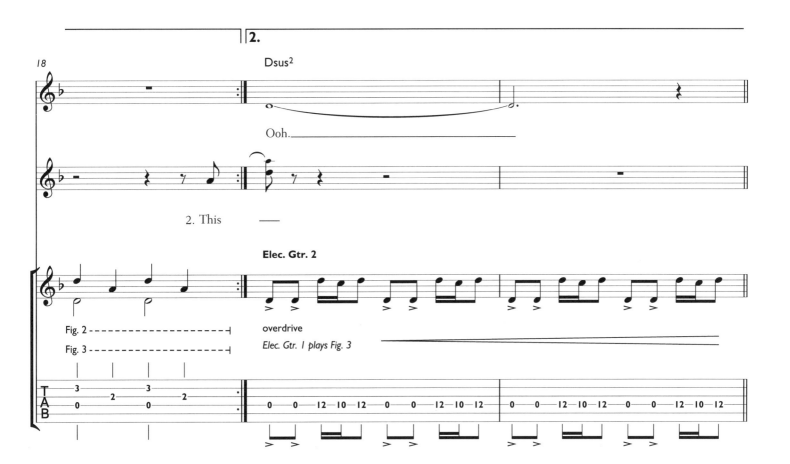

56

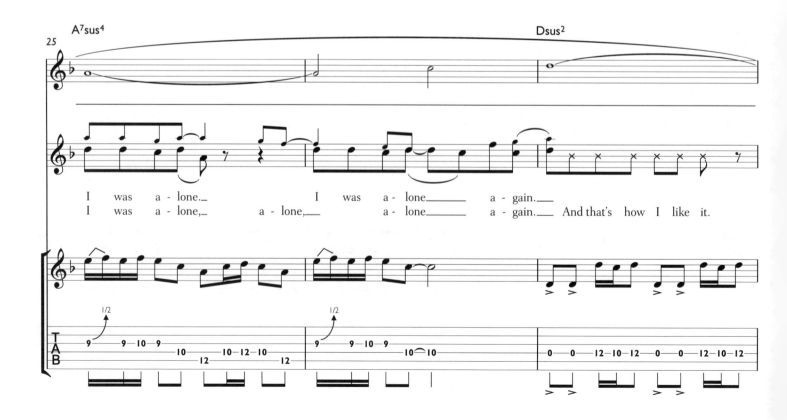

*Play section x6 increasing speed throughout*

**Snare drum**

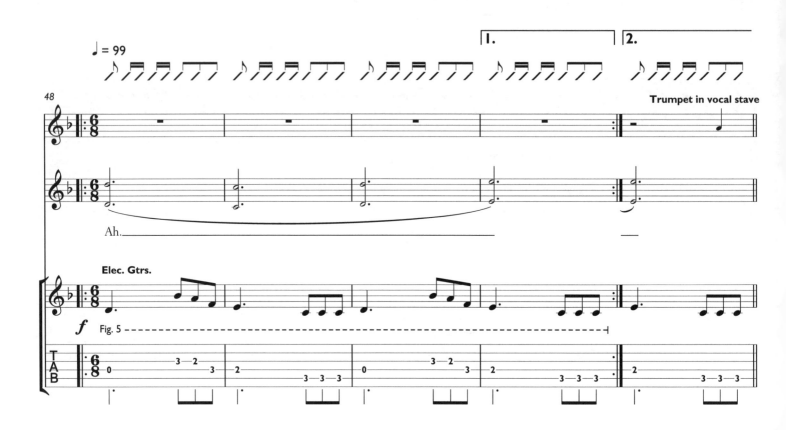

**Trumpet in vocal stave**

Ah._____

**Elec. Gtrs.**

*f* Fig. 5 - - - - - - - - - - - - - - - - - - - - - - - - - - - - -

*ad-lib. cont. sim.*

*Elec. Gtrs. plays Fig 5*

*Elec. Gtrs. plays Fig 5*

*Elec. Gtrs. plays Fig. 5*

*Elec. Gtrs. plays Fig. 5*

*Elec. Gtrs. plays Fig. 5*

© 2006 by International Music Publications Ltd
First published by International Music Publications Ltd in 2006
International Music Publications Ltd is a Faber Music company
3 Queen Square, London WC1N 3AU

Arranged by Alex Davis
Engraved by Camden Music
Edited by Lucy Holliday

Illustrations by Julie Verhoeven
Original Design & Layout by Andy Hayes

Printed in England by Caligraving Ltd
All rights reserved

ISBN10: 0-571-52778-7
EAN13: 978-0-571-52778-6

Reproducing this music in any form is illegal and forbidden by the Copyright, Designs and Patents Act, 1988

To buy Faber Music publications or to find out about the full range of titles available,
please contact your local music retailer or Faber Music sales enquiries:

Faber Music Ltd, Burnt Mill, Elizabeth Way, Harlow, CM20 2HX England
Tel: +44(0)1279 82 89 82 Fax: +44(0)1279 82 89 83
sales@fabermusic.com fabermusic.com